Usborne
Christmas
Decorations
to cut, fold & stick

Illustrated by Caroline Johansson

Designed by Hannah Ahmed

Steps written by Fiona Watt and illustrated by Chris Arrowsmith

How to use this book

This book contains 100 tear-out sheets to make six different types of Christmas decorations. You'll also find some tips for creating more decorations on the inside back cover.

The decorations

Paperchain

Snowflake

Woven heart

Angel

Hanging decoration

Look out for these stars on the paper because they will help you fold the paper correctly.

Folded star

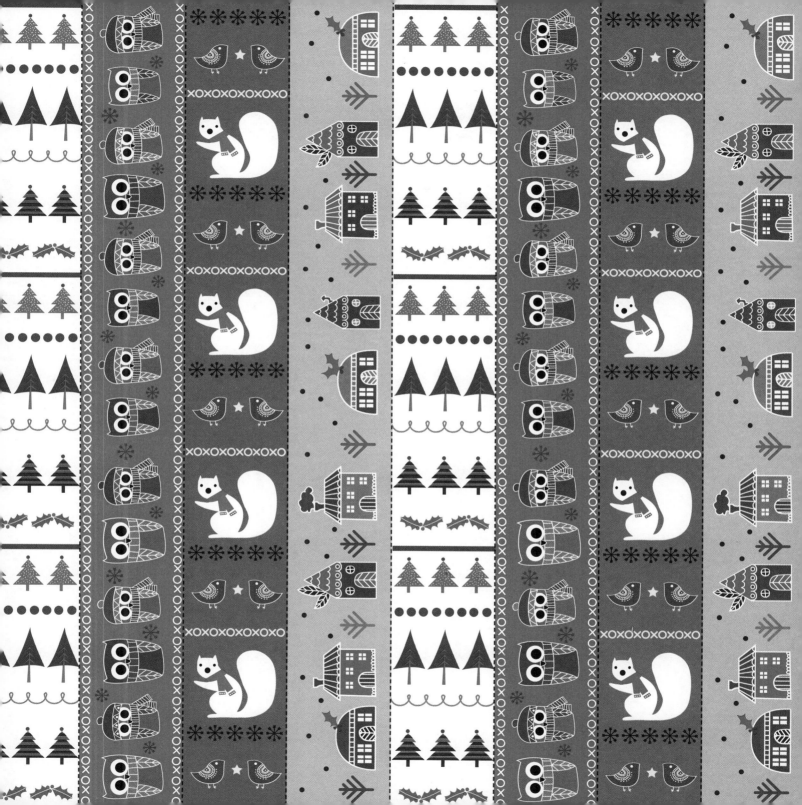

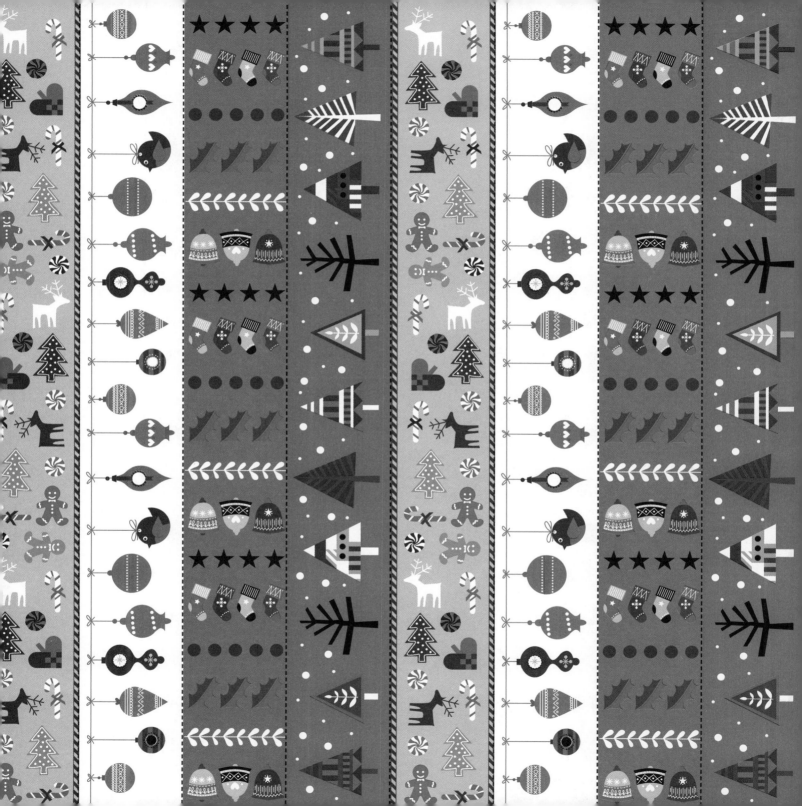

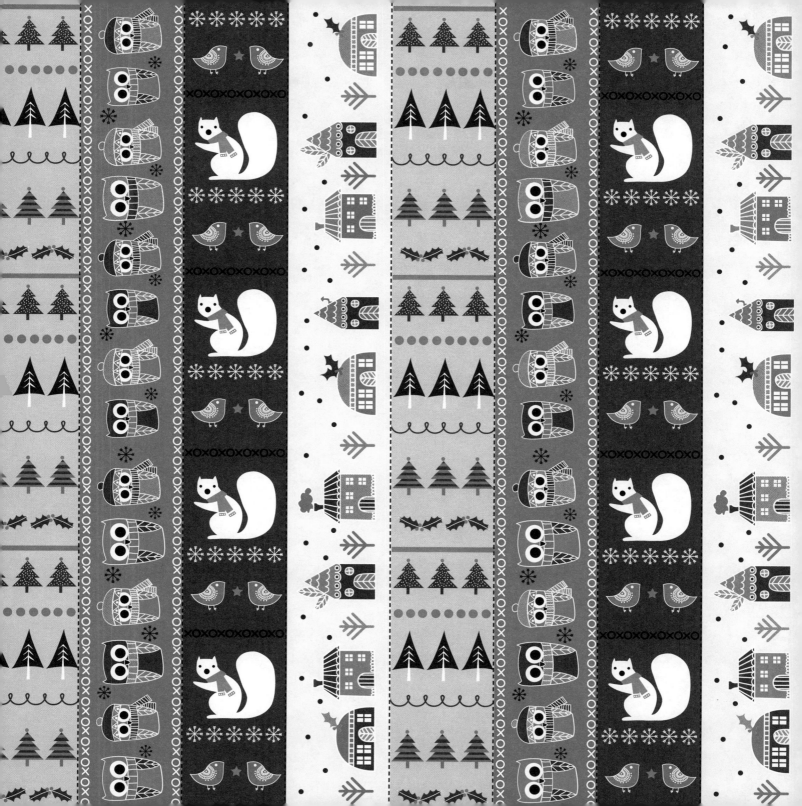

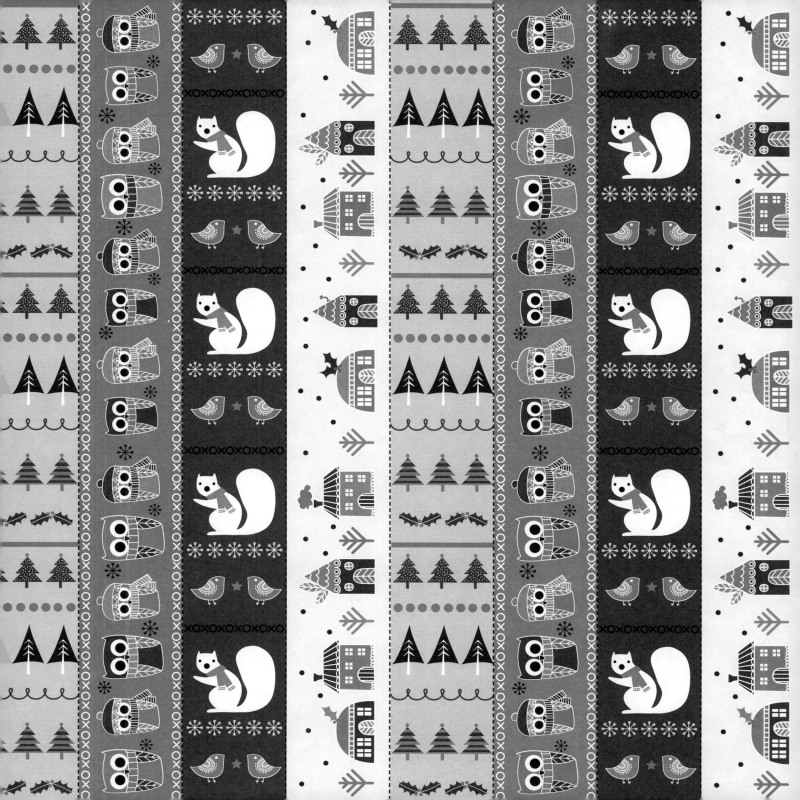

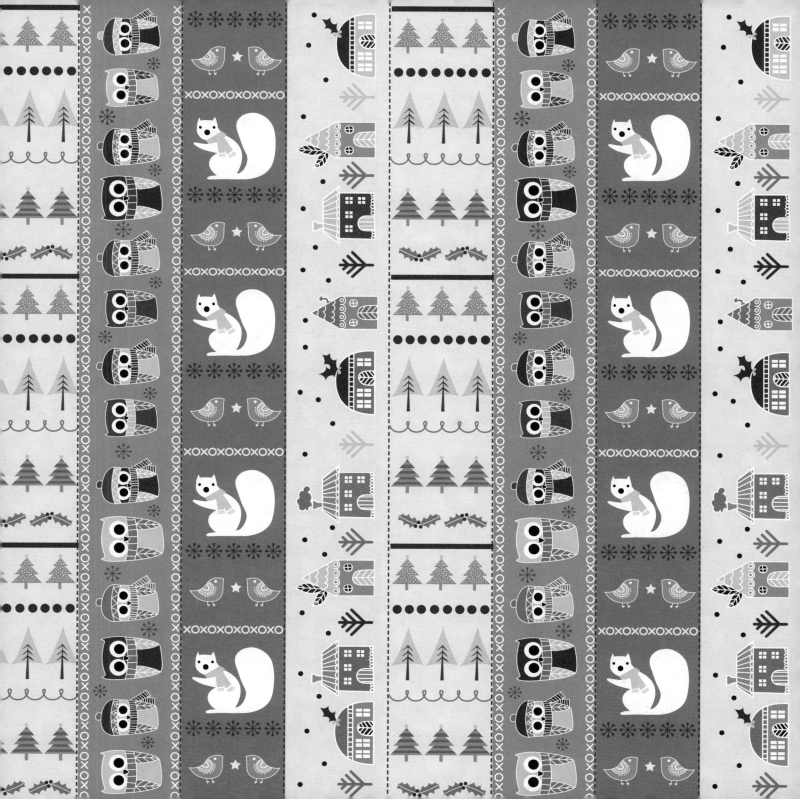

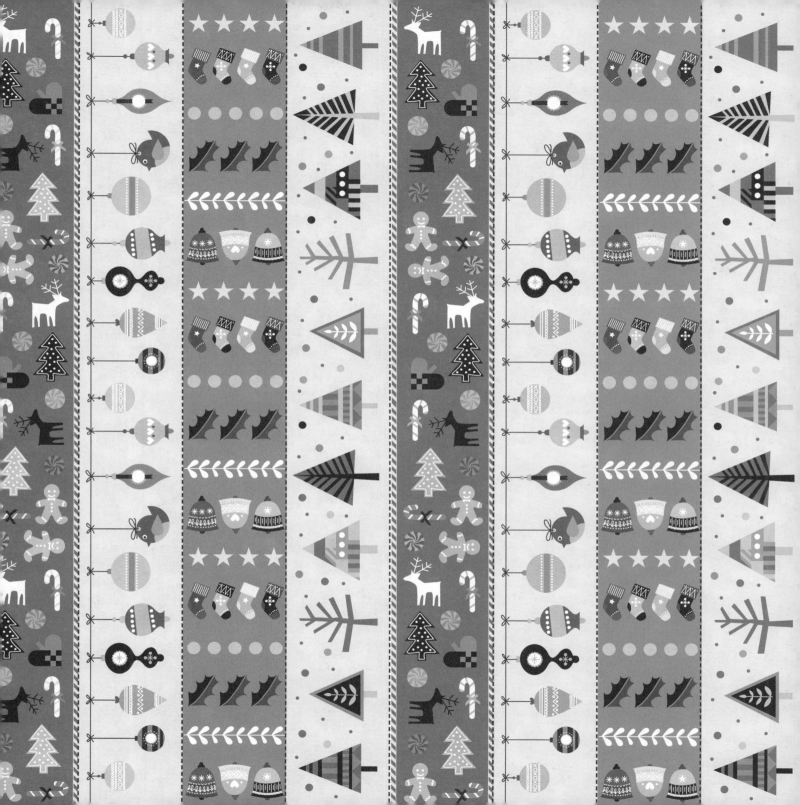

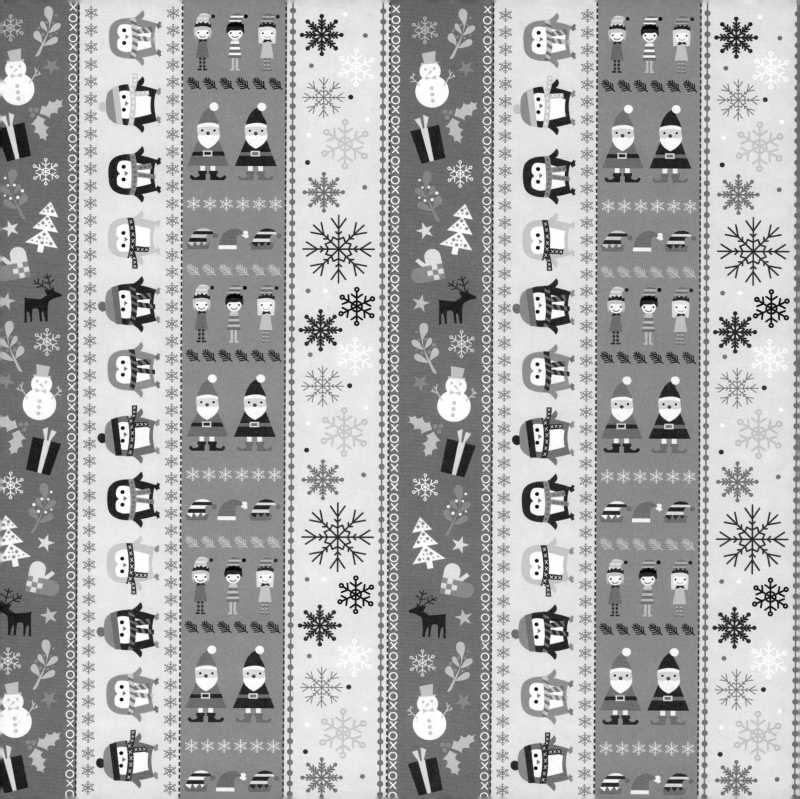

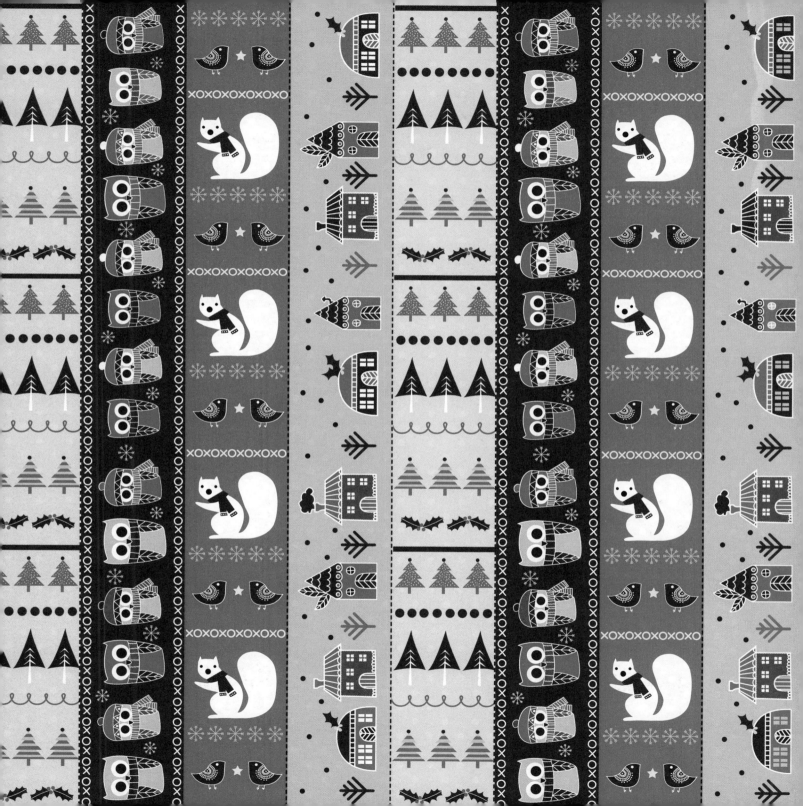

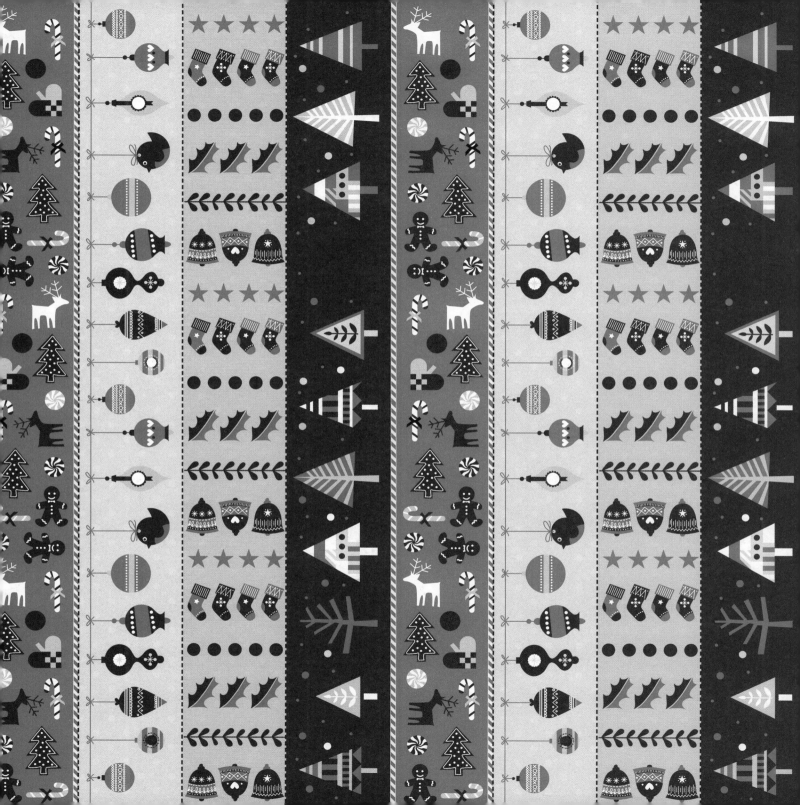

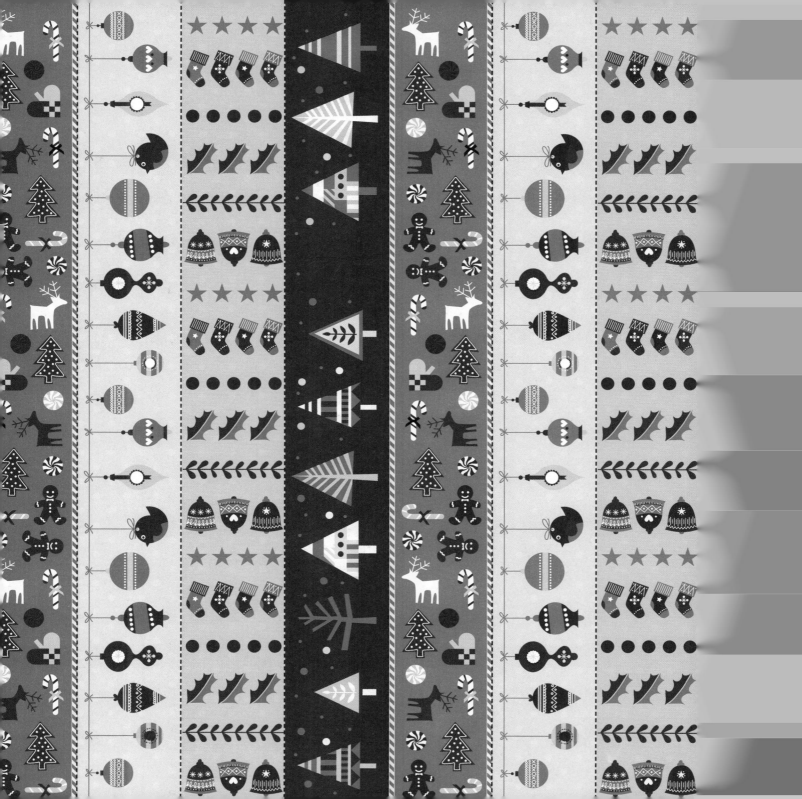

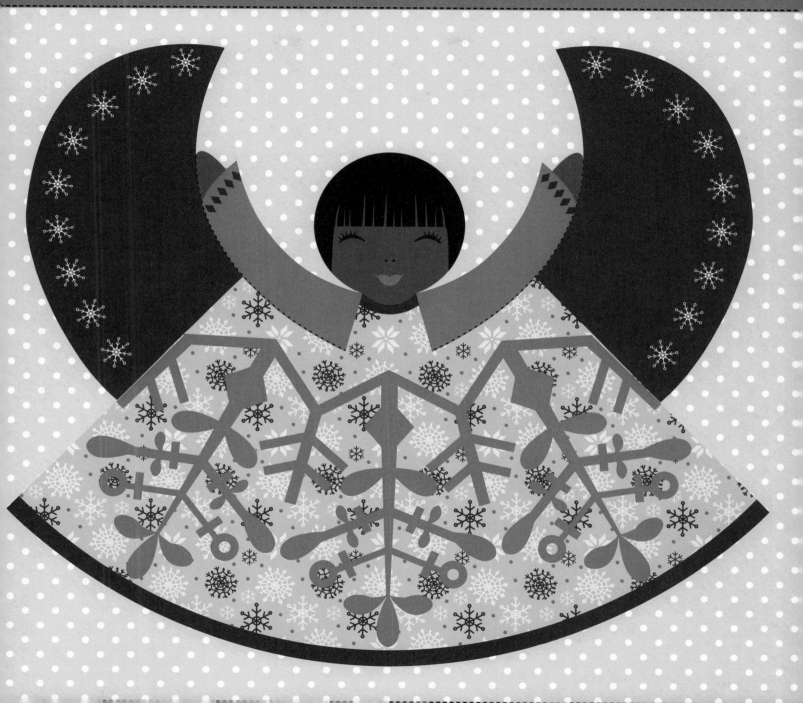

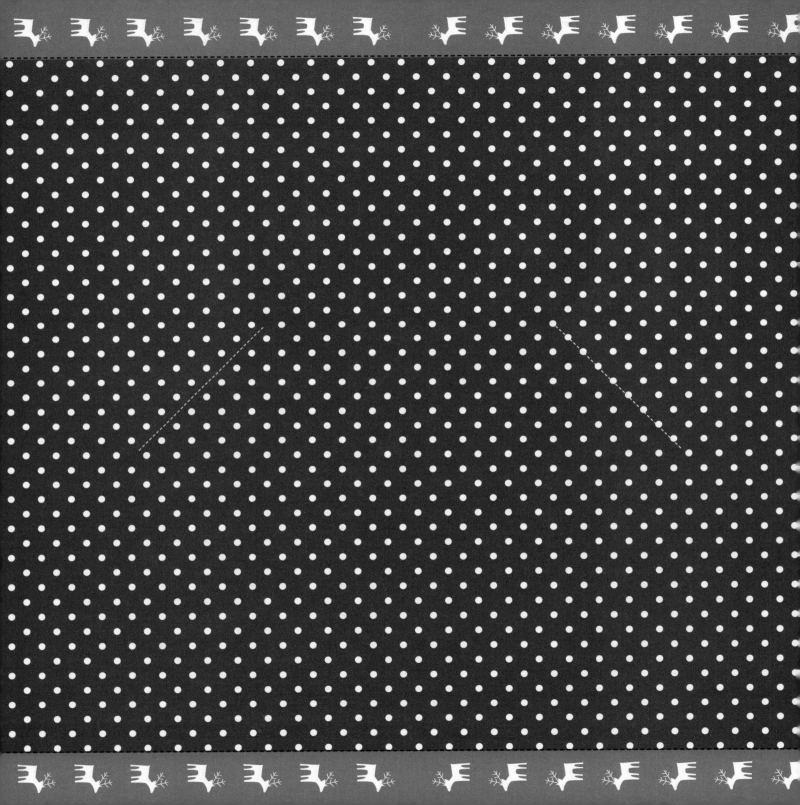

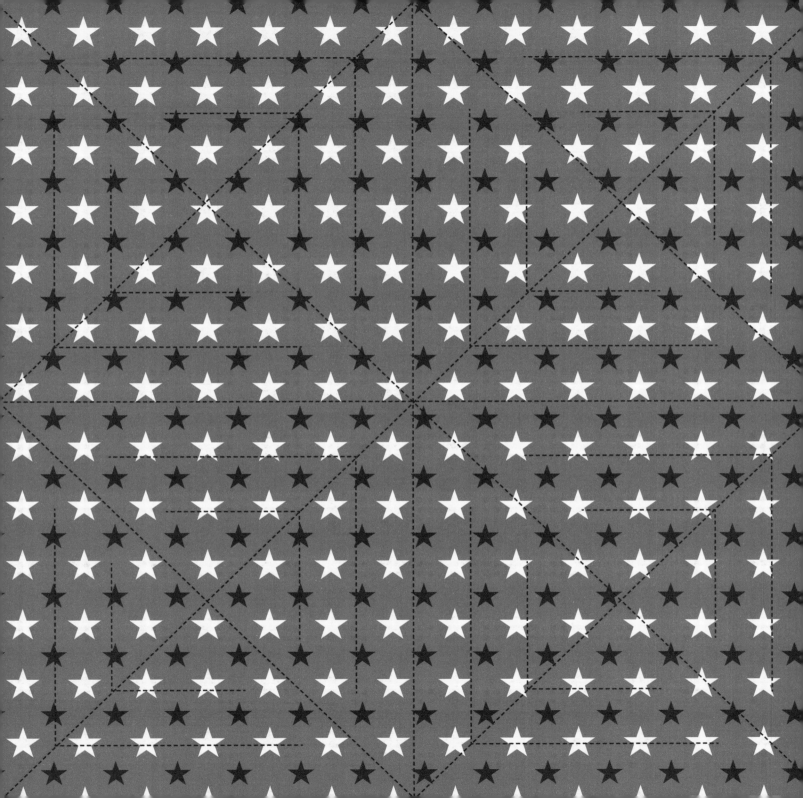

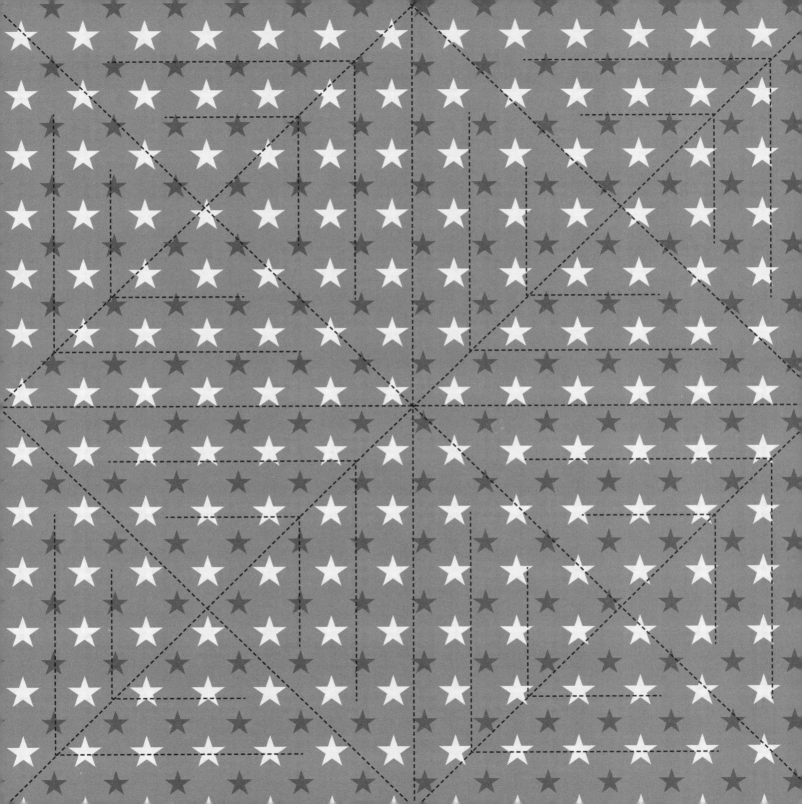

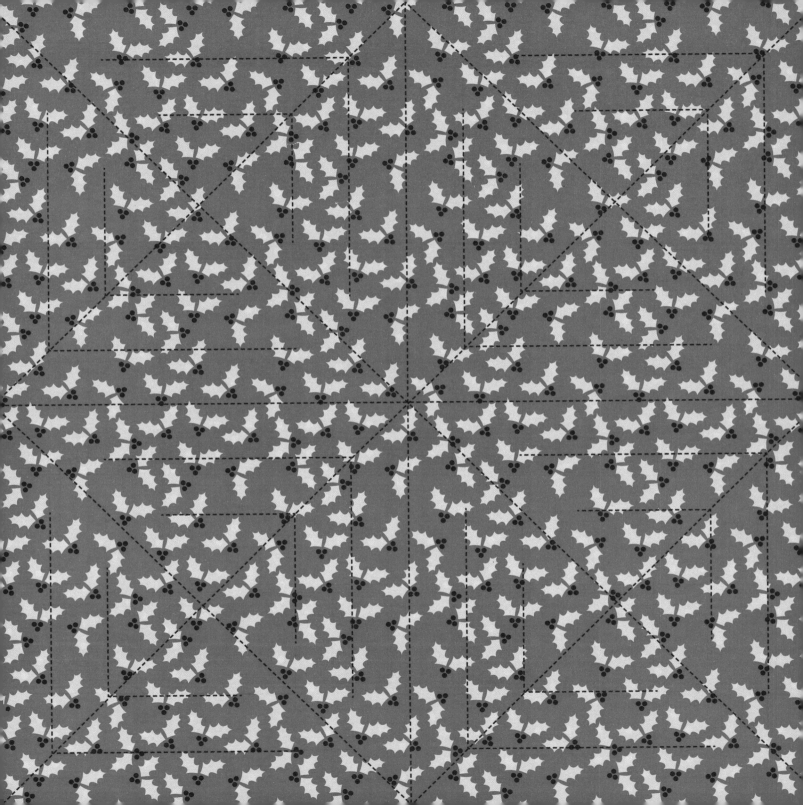

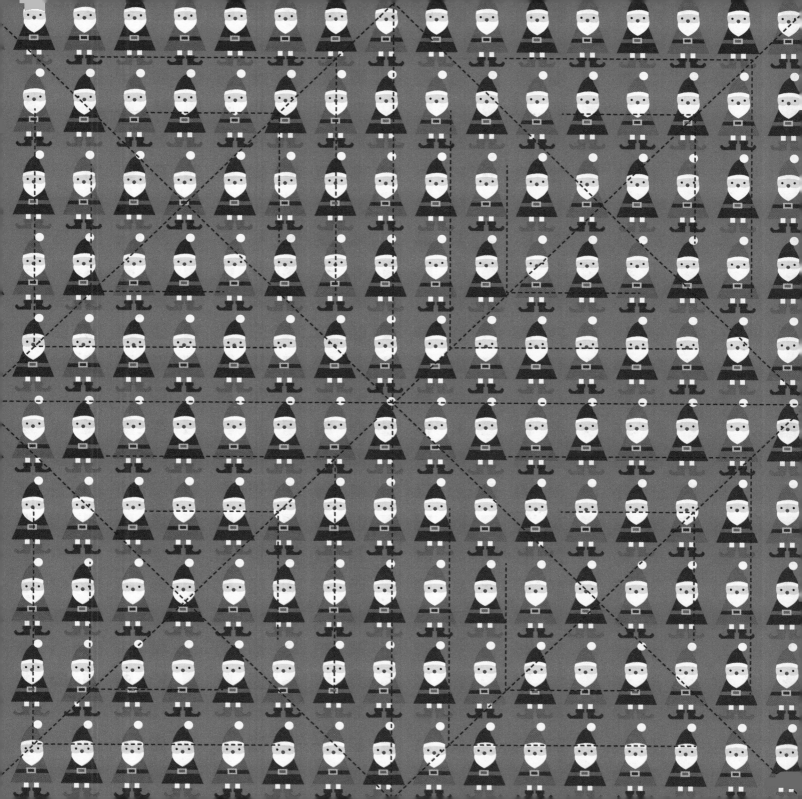

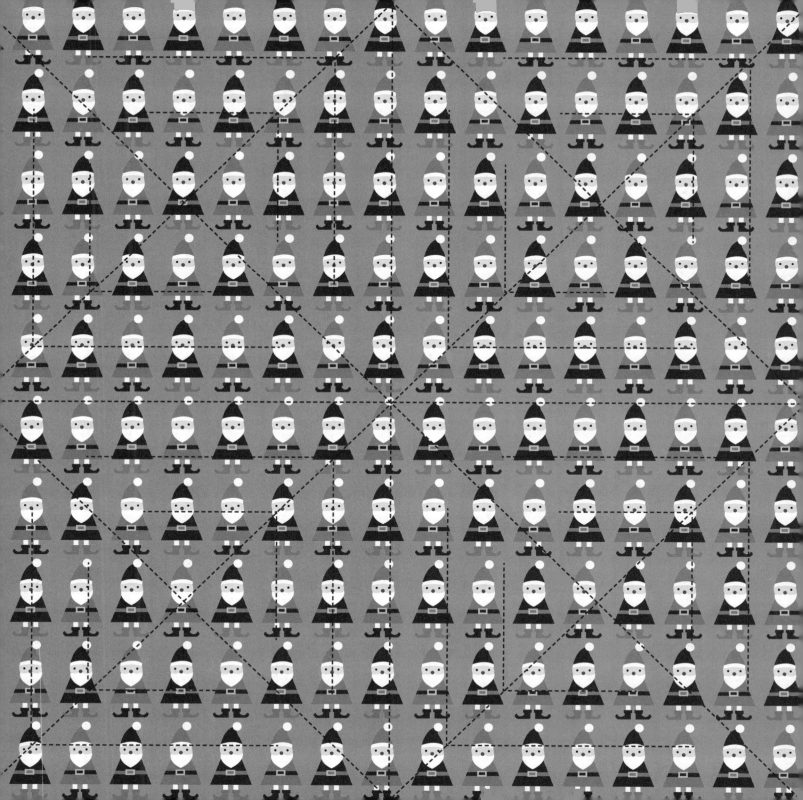

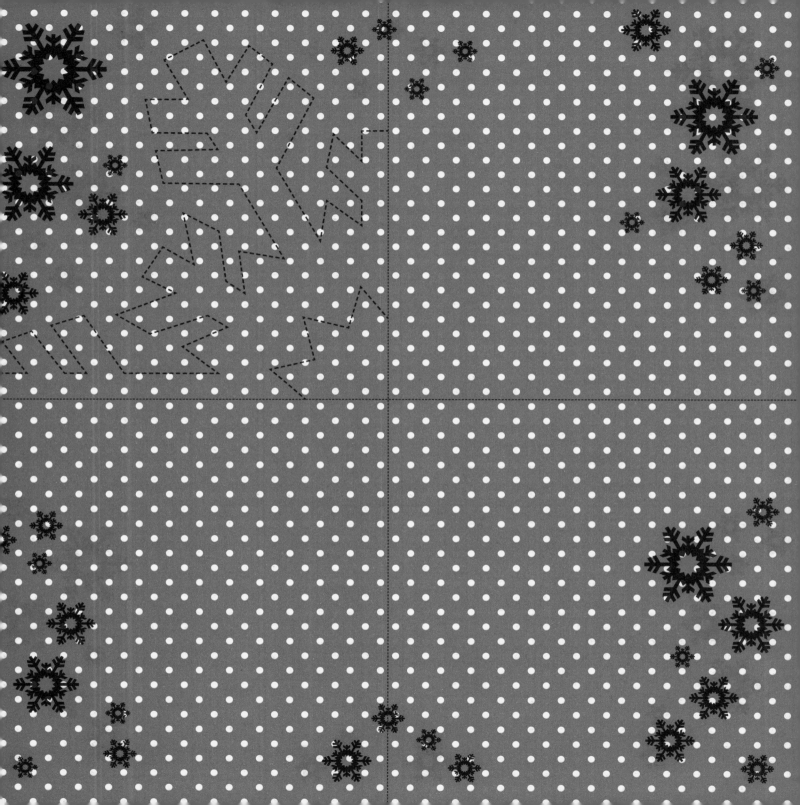

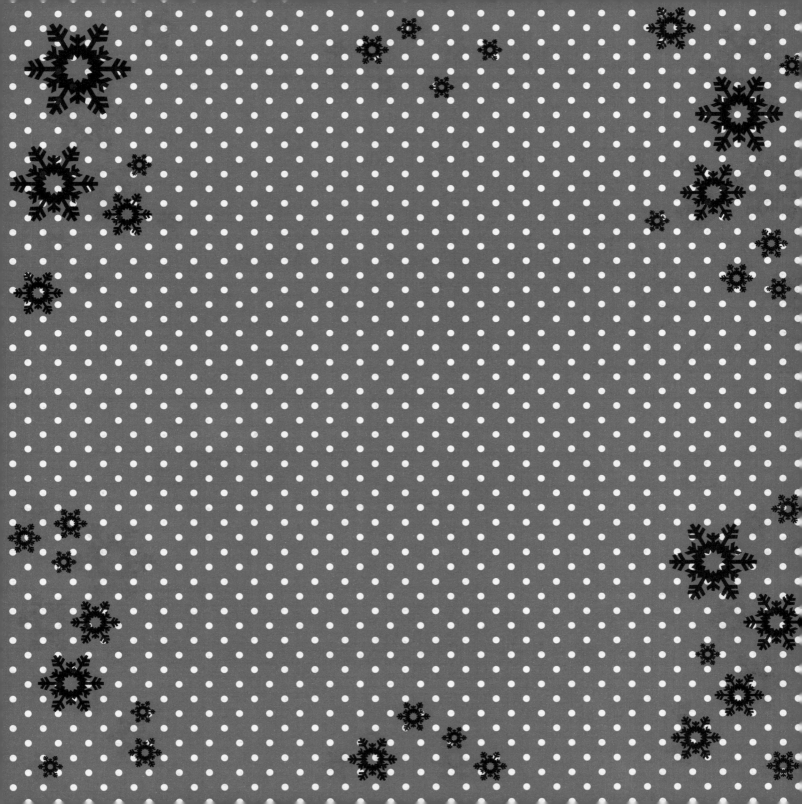

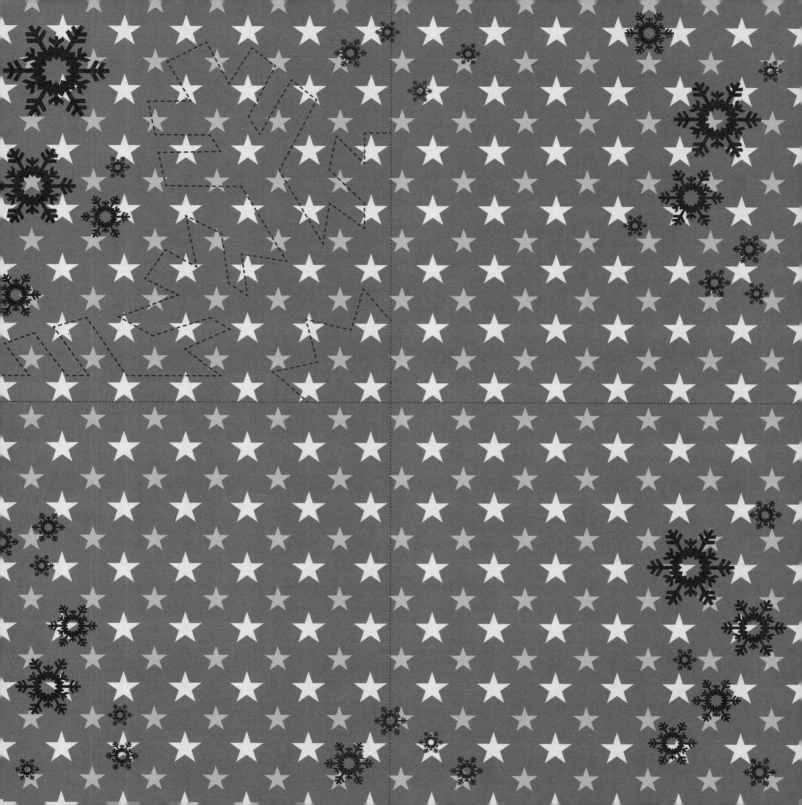

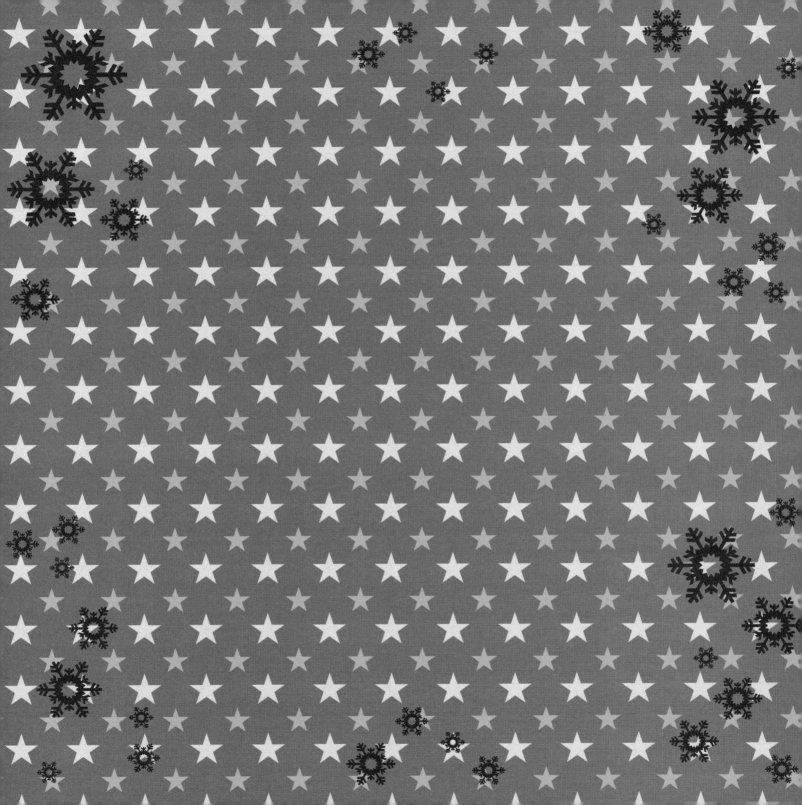

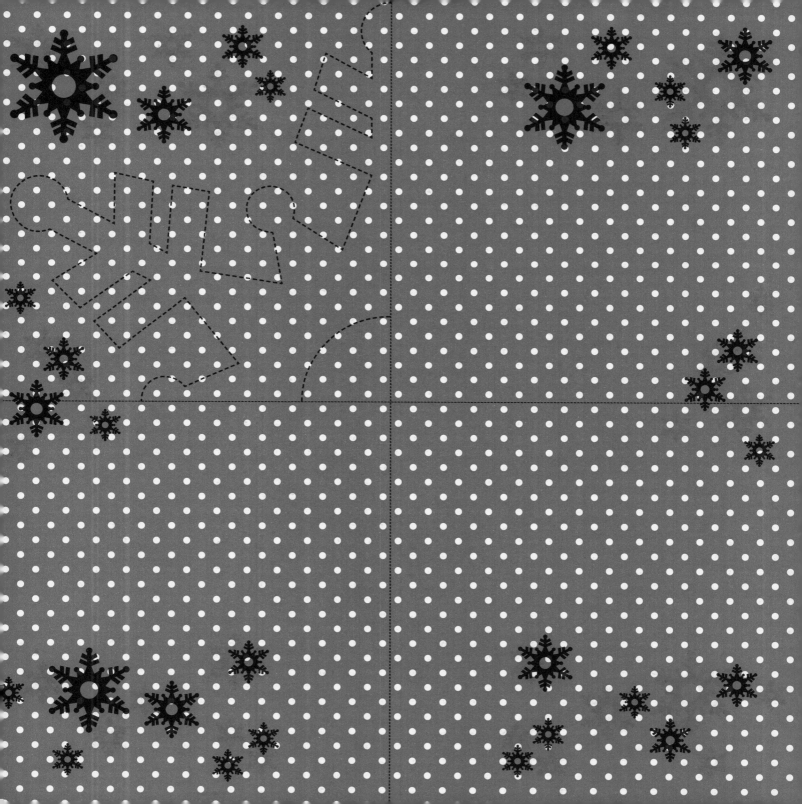

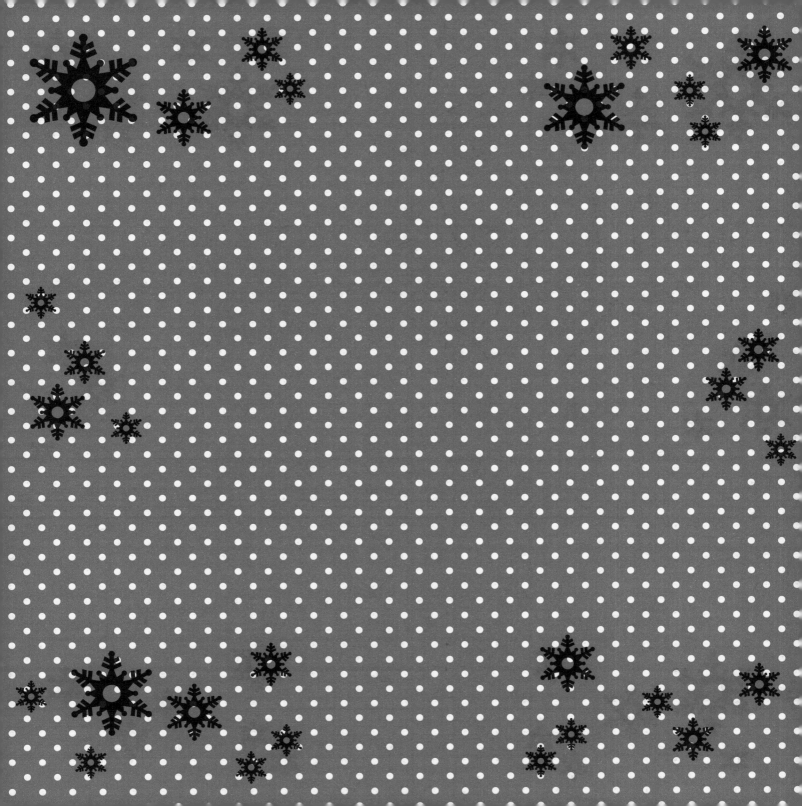

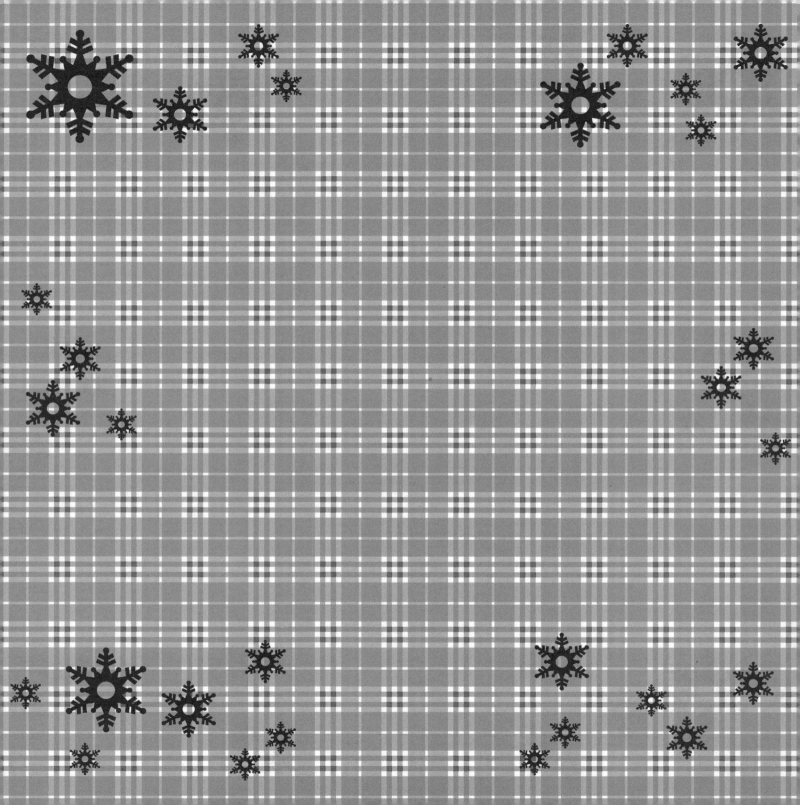

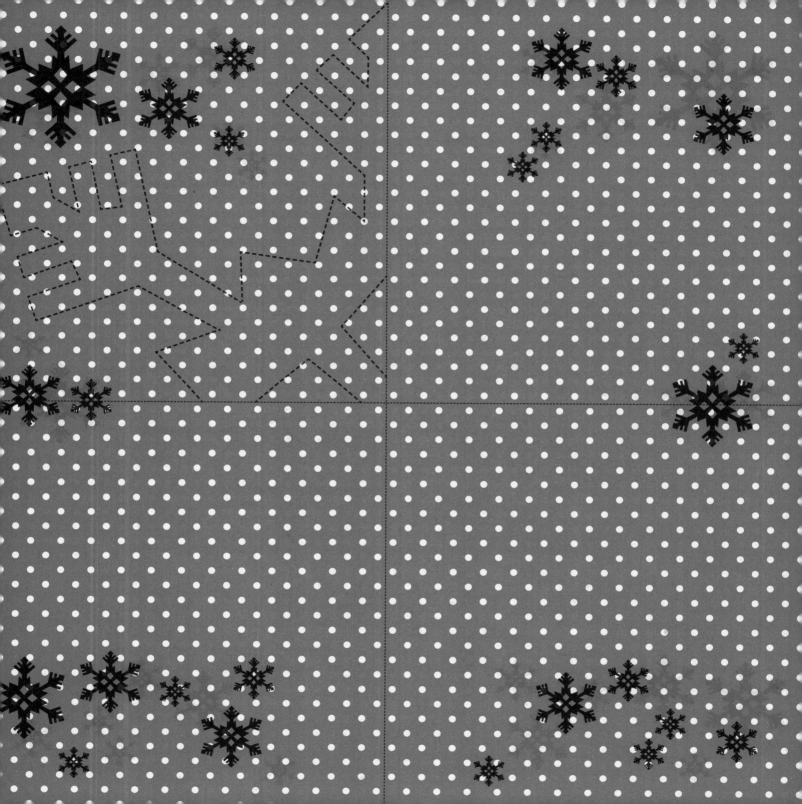

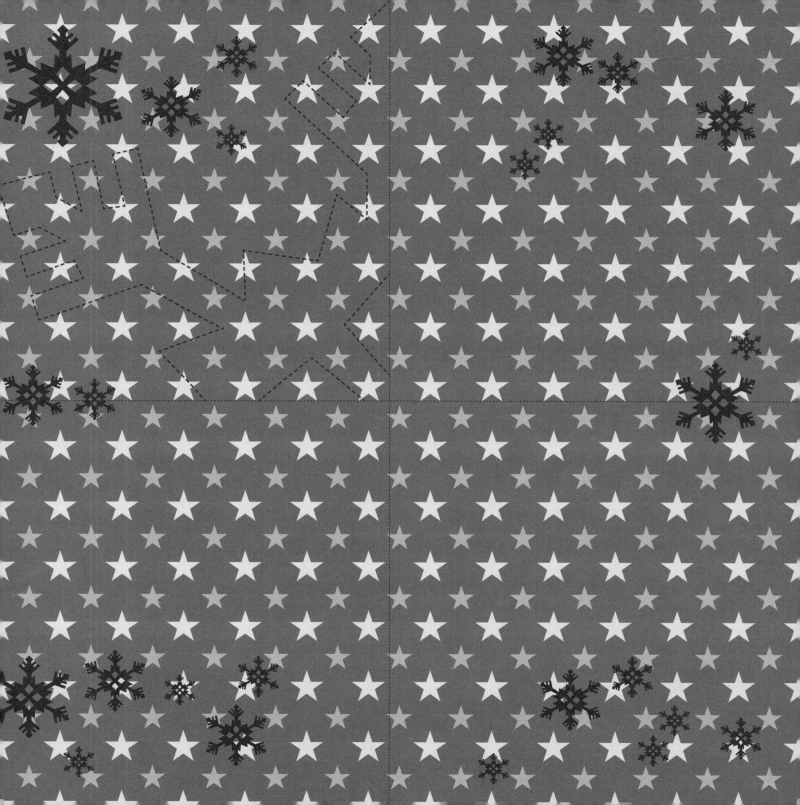

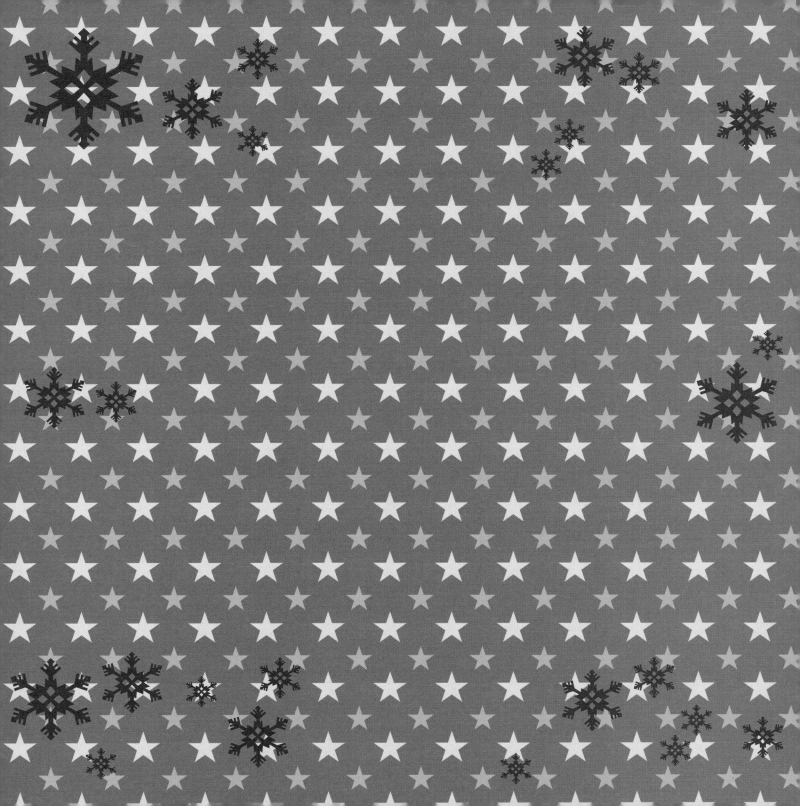

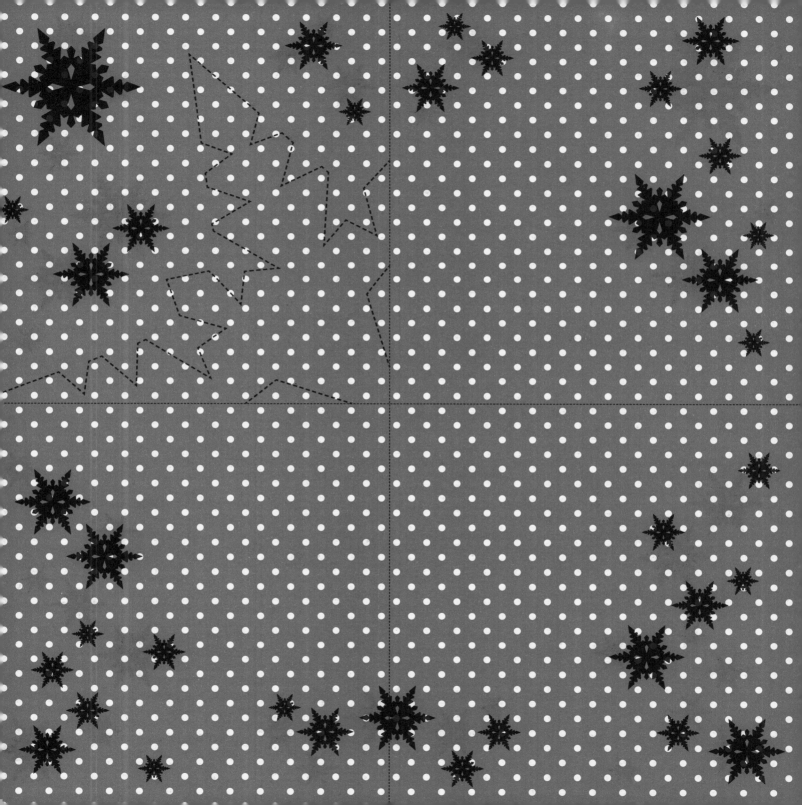

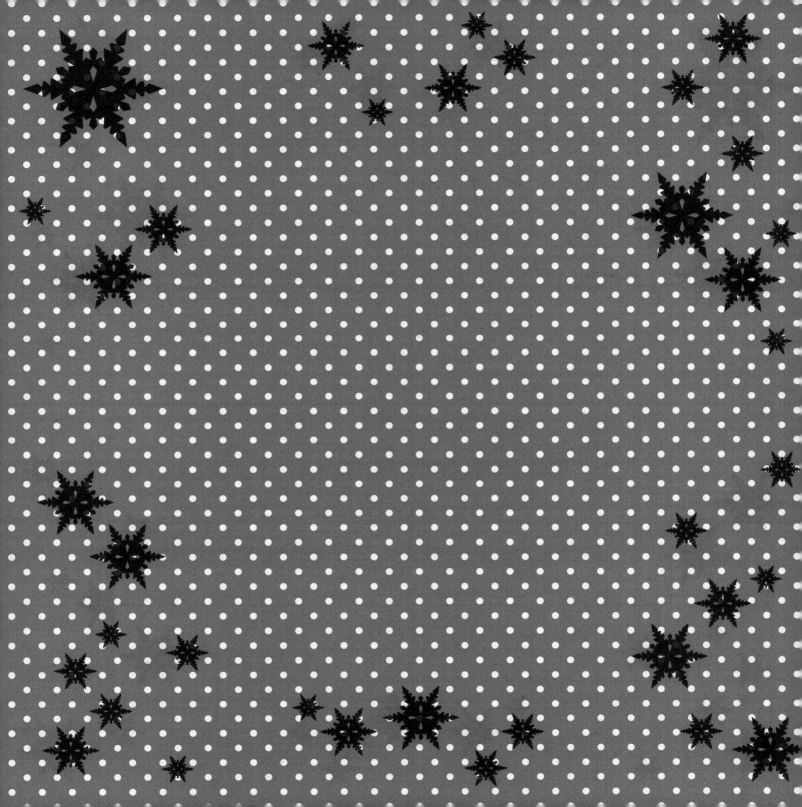

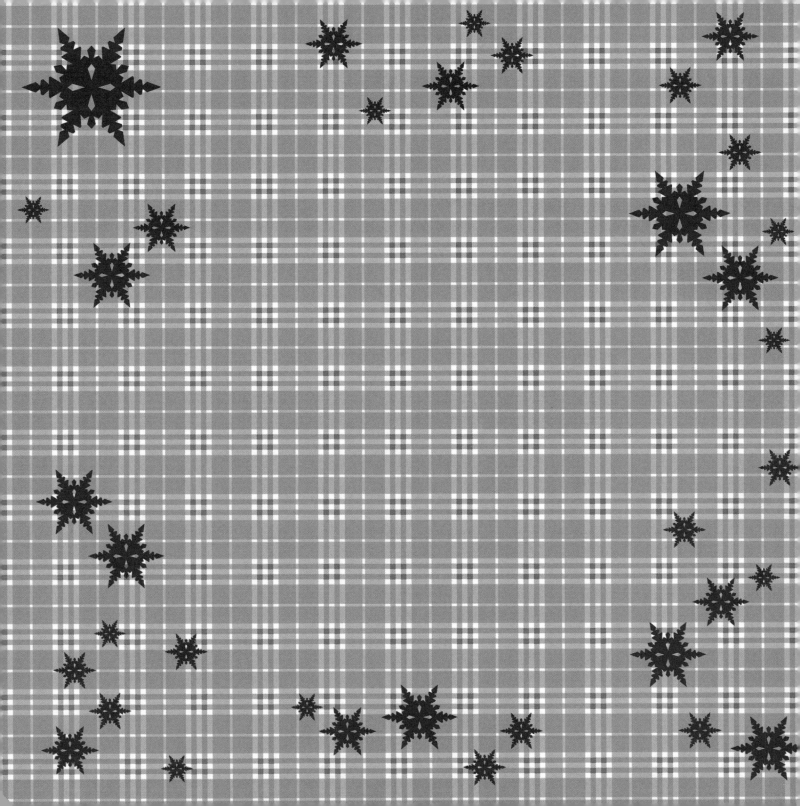

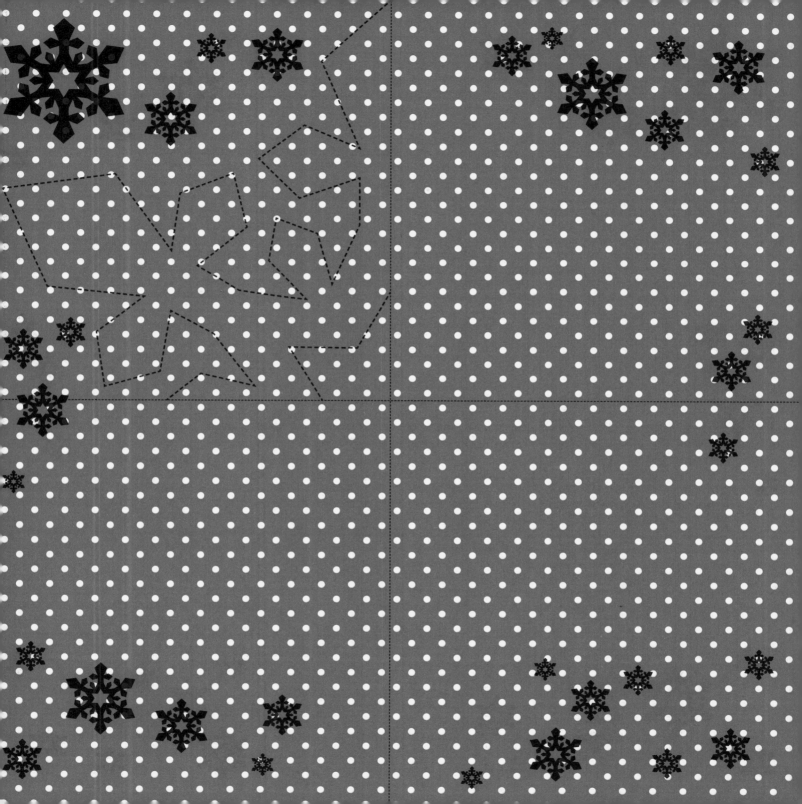

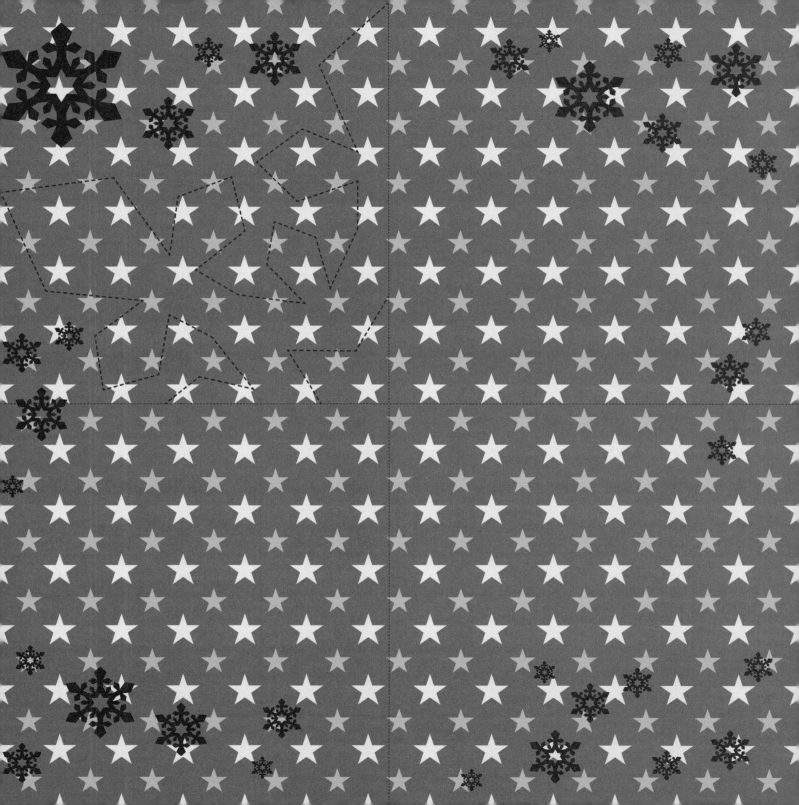

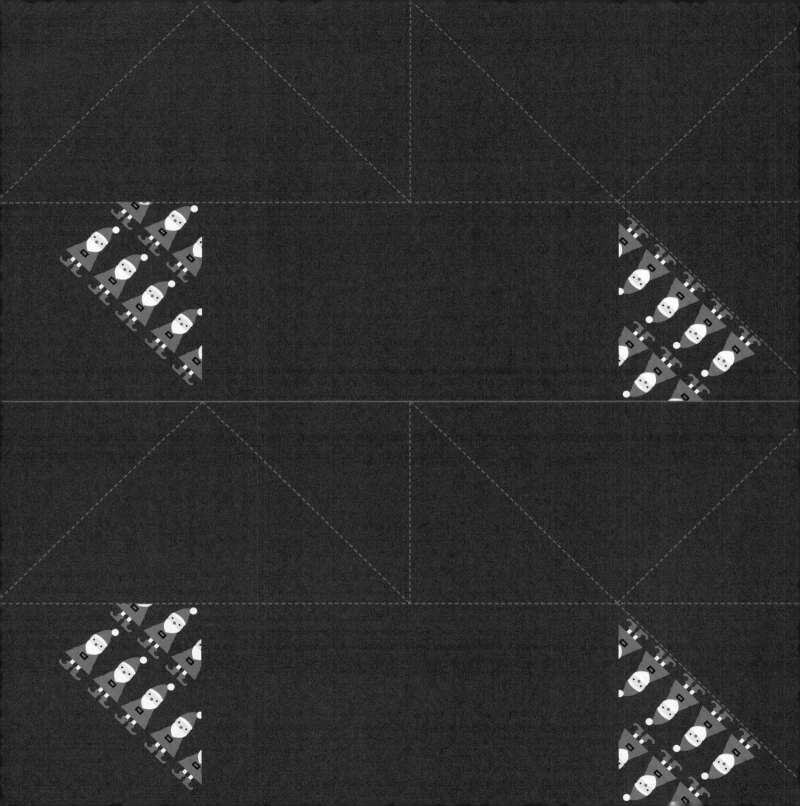

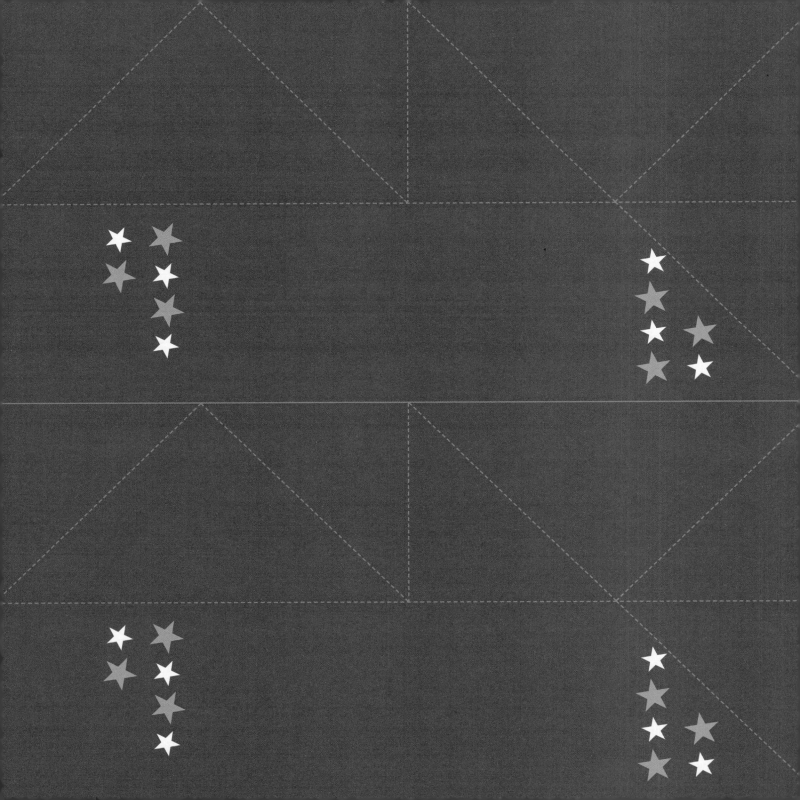

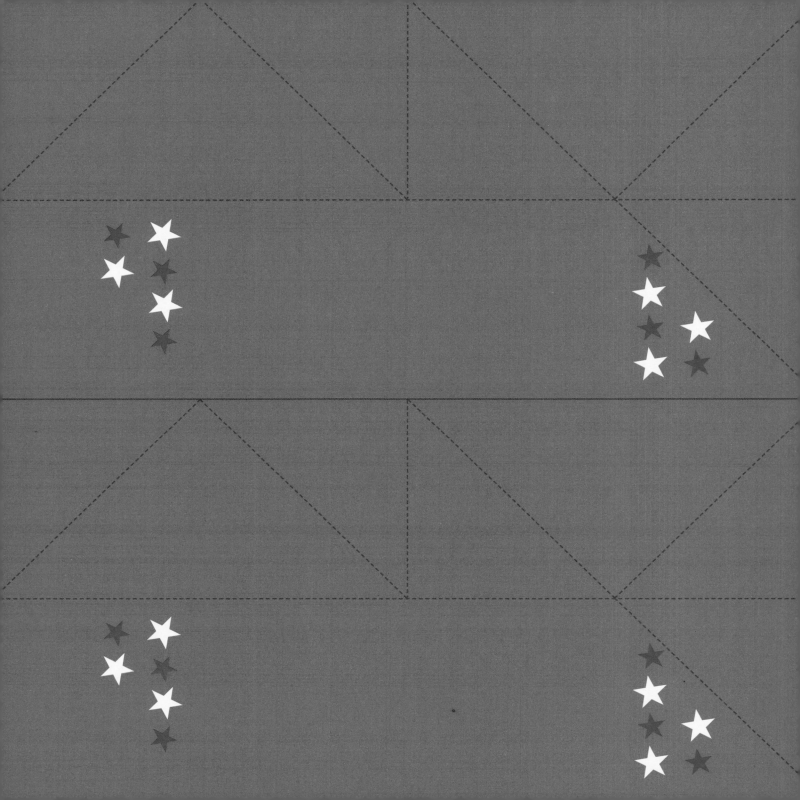

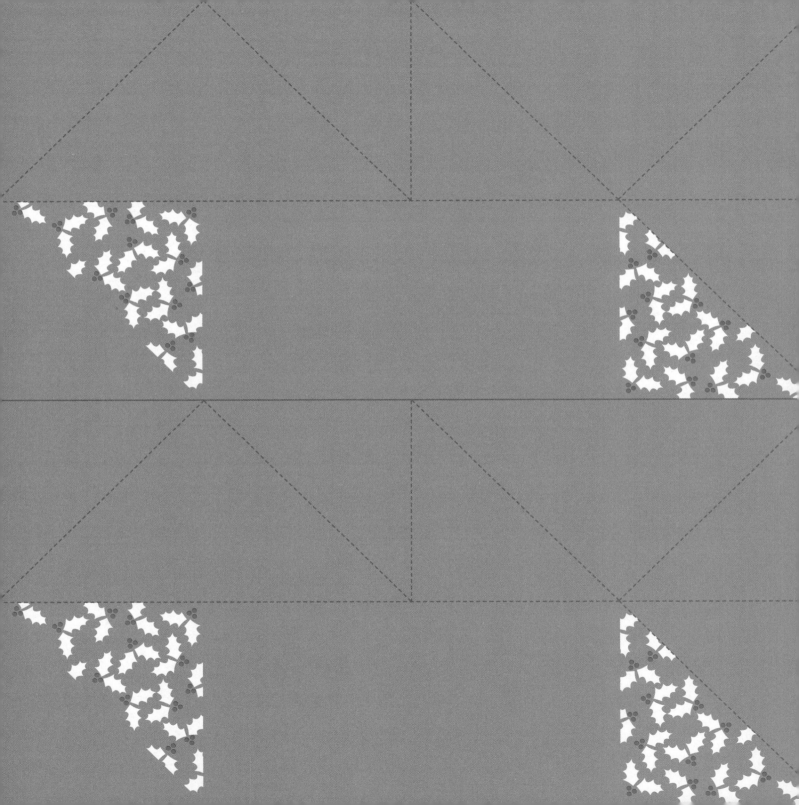

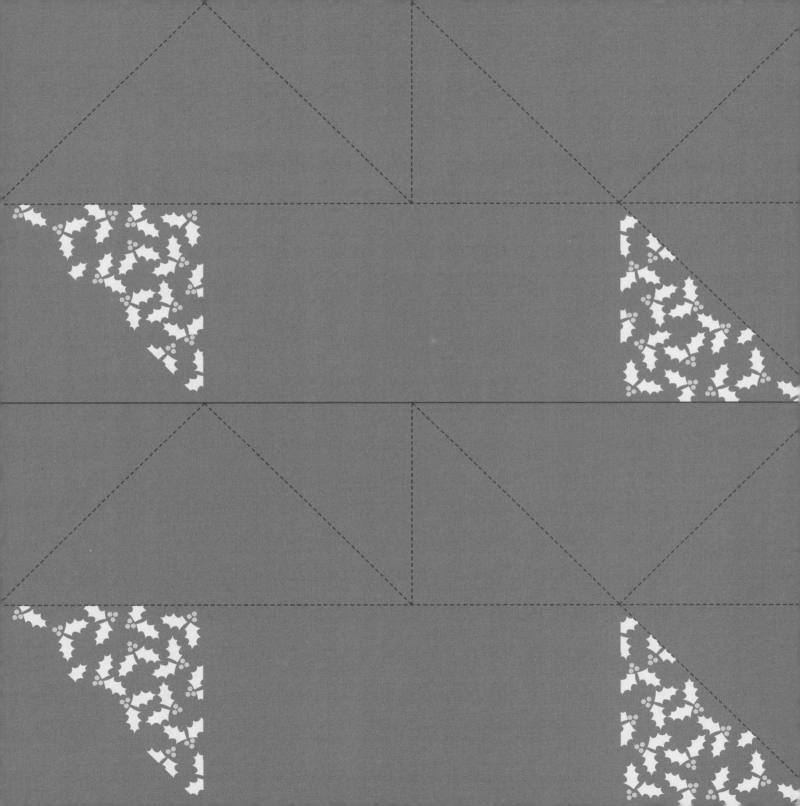

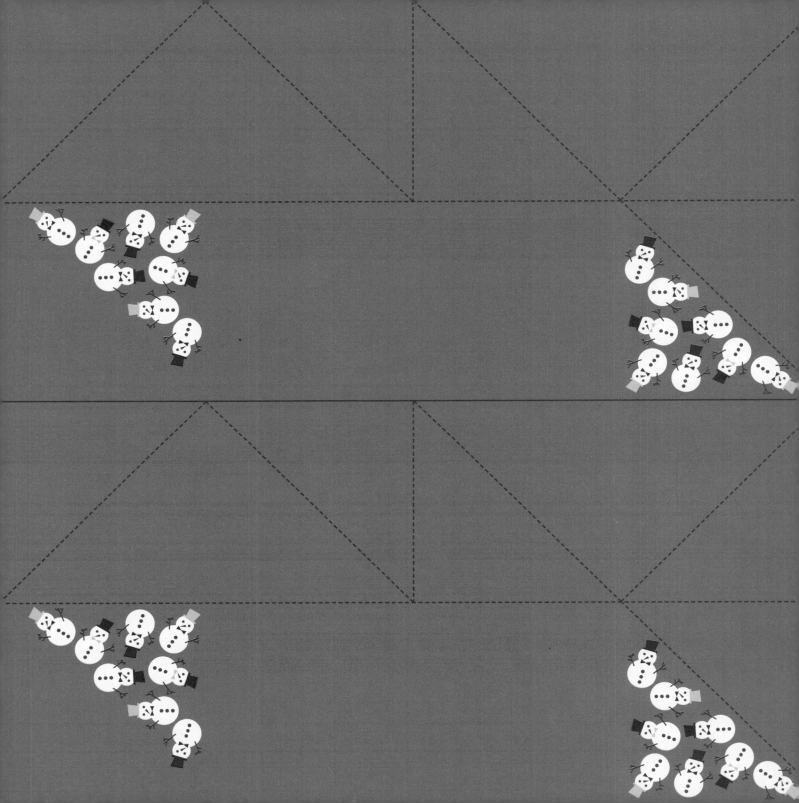

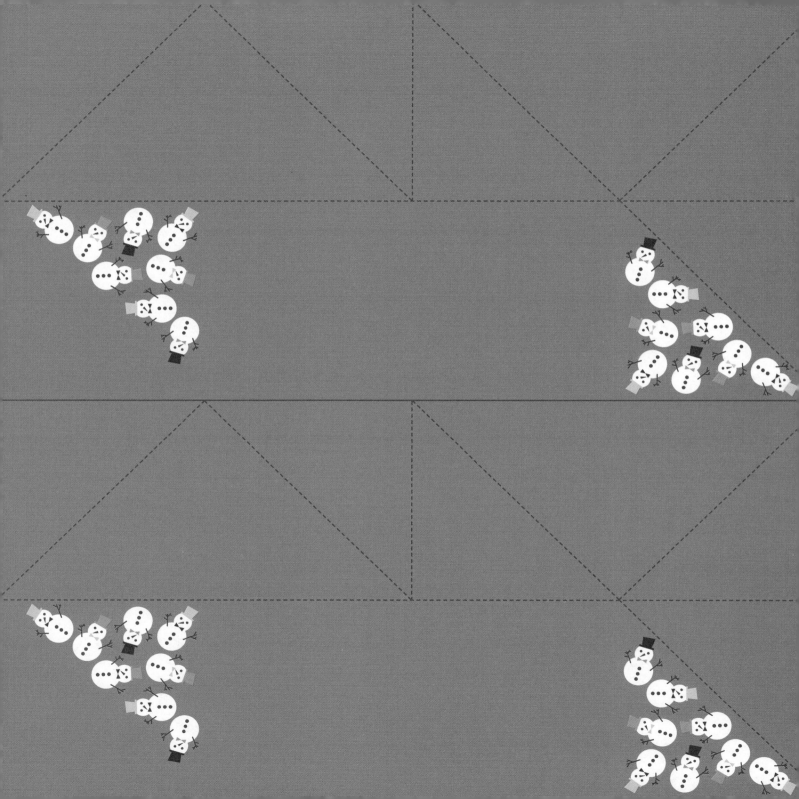

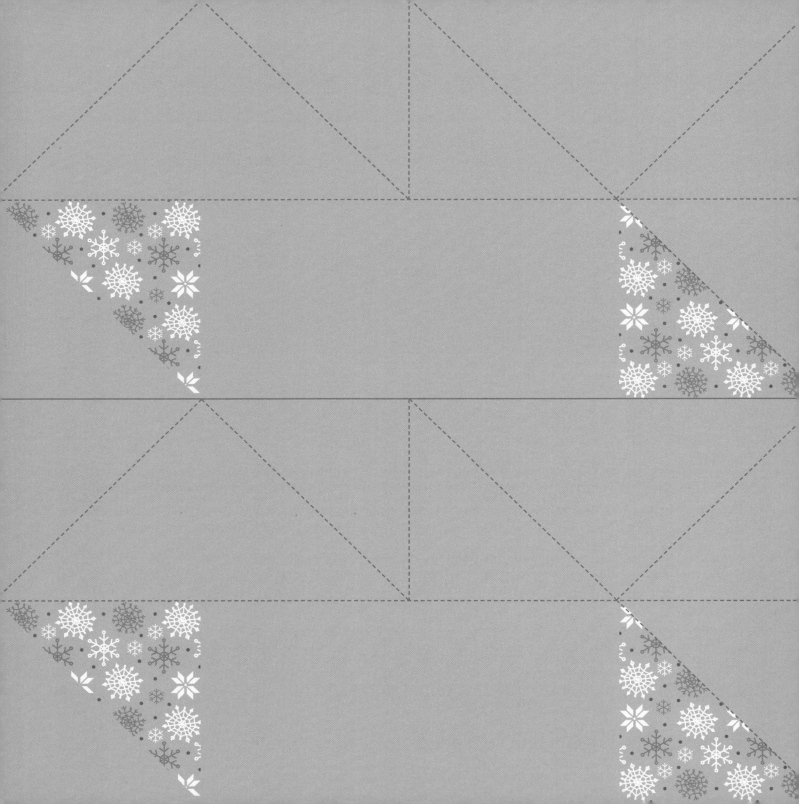

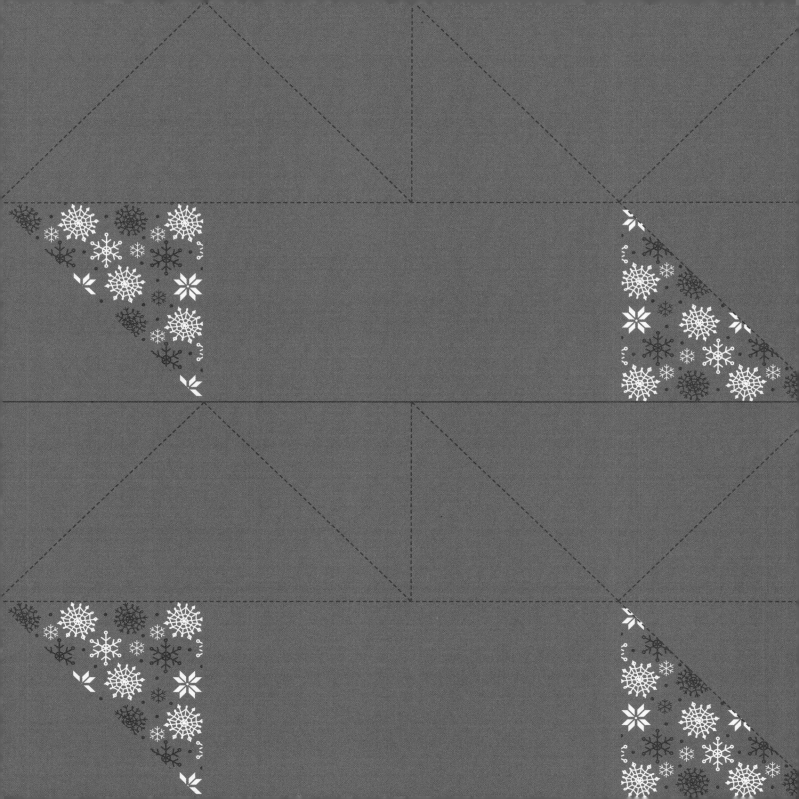

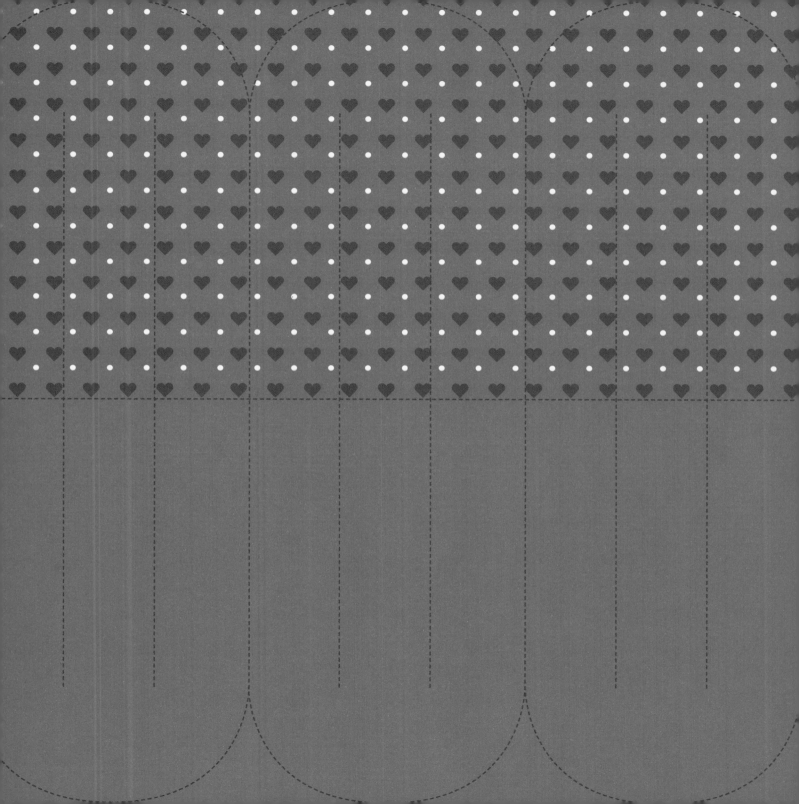

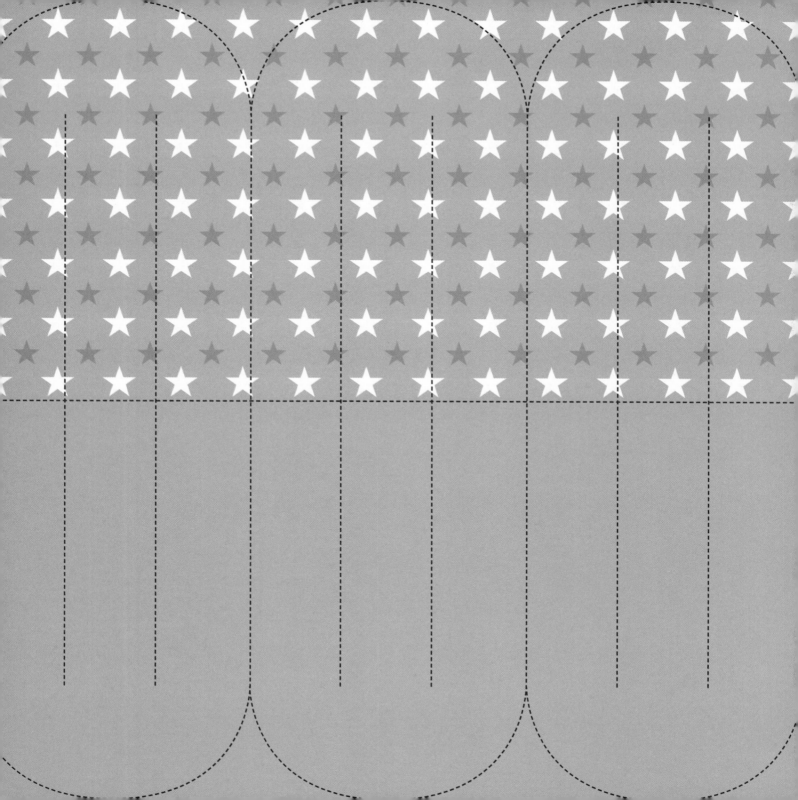